Western Sidereal Astrology
for Beginners

WESTERN

—

SIDEREAL

—

ASTROLOGY

for Beginners

John Savarese

Published by: John Savarese
December 2015, New York City
Author: John Savarese.
Front Cover Amsterdam canal drawing: John Savarese

ISBN-10: 0-692-53126-2
ISBN-13: 978-0-692-53126-6

The astrological charts, speculums and sorted speculums in this book
were generated using Janus astrology software (www.astrology-house.
com) v4.3, Astrology House, 147A Centreway Road, Orewa 0931,
Auckland, New Zealand.

Contents

Preface

This book will enable you to easily and quickly learn the basic principles of Western Sidereal Astrology as championed by Kenneth Bowser in his trailblazing book An Introduction to Western Sidereal Astrology, and by astrologers Cyril Fagan, Bert Fannin and Jack S. Contreras among others (a search on Western Sidereal Astrology and Sidereal Astrology will surely reveal many sidereal astrologers to you). The easy-to-understand information and illustrations I provide support this new approach, which actually originates from some of the most effective astrological techniques used in the ancient world.

> —*John Savarese, B.A., M.A., NCGR–PAA*
> *(National Council for Geocosmic Research–*
> *Professional Astrologers' Alliance), Level 3*

Chapter 1

PRECESSION

———

In the vast expanse of outer space, the dynamic mechanisms of stellar and planetary motion are everywhere, driven by subtle yet enormously powerful astrophysical forces. Planetary bodies spin and revolve around stars that revolve around star clusters ejected from the centers of galaxies. Some stars revolve around other stars, some stars are consumed by black holes, moons revolve around planets, comets, asteroids, meteors zoom by; this and more is all part of the cosmos. And in our particular local part of the cosmos, we find the Sun, planets and moons of our solar system and of course our home planet Earth.

Pervasive throughout the universe is the phenomenon of precession, which was discovered by Hipparchus of Nicaea in the Hellenistic Period. Earth which is tilted at an angle of about 23 and one half degrees while revolving around the Sun spins (rotates) around its axis at this angle. Think of the Earth's axis as being a line between the North Pole and South Pole cutting through the center of Earth and extending itself beyond the North Pole and the South Pole into outer space. Earth spinning on its axis of 23 and one half degrees causes a wobble in Earth's axis which will cause the axis to gyrate and trace a complete circle of 360 degrees above Earth in a very long period of time. The same happens when you look down at a top spinning on an angle of 23 and one half degrees. The top's axis you are looking down upon will also trace a complete circle of 360 degrees above the top, but of course in a very short period of time.

Because of the wobble in Earth's axis, and as seen from Earth, the stars in the ecliptic (zodiac) will be seen to shift backward or "precess" one degree during the span of 72 solar years which equals 72 Vernal Equinox to Vernal Equinox cycles. After 2,150 solar years, a total shift or precession of 30 degrees occurs, causing the preceding constellation of stars in a sign of the zodiac to be seen from Earth when the Sun rises at zero degrees latitude on the Equator at the beginning of the next Vernal Equinox.

After 25,800 solar years, a grand total shift of 360 degrees will occur, so the original constellation of stars seen 25,800 solar years ago in the ecliptic will again be seen from Earth when the Sun rises at zero degrees latitude on the Equator at the beginning of the next Vernal Equinox. The natural phenomenon of precession determines the constellations in the ecliptic that are seen from Earth during successive Vernal Equinox to Vernal Equinox cycles as time passes by.

The ancient great astronomer Ptolemy observed in 221 AD that the Sun rose at zero degrees Aries on the Vernal Equinox at the end of the Age of Aries, 2,150 years after it started rising at the beginning of the Age of Aries in 1,930 BC. Now in 2015 after 1,794 years from 221 AD, the Sun actually rises on the Vernal Equinox at approximately 5 degrees Pisces because of precession and not at zero degrees Aries as it did in 221 AD when Ptolemy observed it doing so. As seen from Earth, the stars have shifted ever so slightly backwards approximately 24 degrees since 221 AD due to precession.

Because of what is known as the Precession of the Equinoxes, defined as successive periods of 2,150 solar years of precession in each sign, we were in the Age of Aries, we are currently in the Age of Pisces, and we will be in the Age of Aquarius, which will not occur until five more degrees of precession occur at which time the Sun will be seen rising at the Vernal Equinox at 29 degrees 59 minutes 59 seconds Aquarius. It takes just 5 more degrees of precession, or 350 more solar years. Then for 2,150 solar years, the Sun will rise in position with the stars of Aquarius on the Vernal Equinox. It takes 25,800 solar years of precession to complete a 360 degree cycle going back through all the ages of the 12 signs of the zodiac. In this great period of solar time, Earth's axis will gyrate and trace a circle of 360 degrees.

Since Western Sidereal Astrology is based on sidereal time, it is appropriate at this point to describe sidereal time, and the differences between sidereal time and solar time (also known as tropical time). Essentially, a sidereal year is based on Earth orbiting the Sun with respect to the stars while a solar, tropical year is based on Earth orbiting the Sun from the perspective of the Sun as seen from Earth.

Chapter 2

A SIDEREAL YEAR AND
A SOLAR YEAR

———

At the Vernal Equinox in the Northern hemisphere (Autumnal Equinox in the Southern hemisphere), a sidereal year ("star" based year) on Earth begins when the Sun, as seen from Earth is in position with particular stars in the zodiac (ecliptic). At the end of the sidereal year after Earth completes a 360 degree revolution around the Sun, the backdrop of stars the Sun was in position with at the beginning of the sidereal year has shifted a bit. The Sun rising again at the new Vernal Equinox is seen to be in position with stars that are, in the zodiac, a tad before the stars the Sun was in position with at the beginning of the previous sidereal year. During the course of many sidereal years, the Sun rising at each Vernal Equinox is seen to be positioned more and more among the preceding stars of the zodiac. As seen from Earth, this shift in the stars is due to precession.

A sidereal year consists of 365.25636 solar days and it is 19 solar minutes and 56 seconds longer than a solar year. A solar year (or tropical year) in the Northern hemisphere starts:

- when the Sun is seen at sunrise at the beginning of Spring, rising on the Equator (at the Vernal Equinox).
- three months later, the Sun will be seen at sunrise at the beginning of Summer, rising on the Tropic of Cancer (at the Summer Solstice).

- three months later, the Sun will be seen at sunrise at the beginning of Autumn, rising on the Equator again (at the Autumnal Equinox).
- three months later, the Sun will be seen at sunrise at the beginning of Winter, rising on the Tropic of Capricorn (at the Winter Solstice).
- three months later, the Sun will be seen at sunrise again at the beginning of Spring, rising once again on the Equator (at the next Vernal Equinox).

This 12 month Vernal Equinox to Vernal Equinox cycle from the beginning of one Spring to the beginning of the next Spring defines a solar year in the Northern hemisphere.

A solar year (or tropical year) in the Southern hemisphere starts:

- when the Sun is seen at sunrise at the beginning of Autumn, rising on the Equator (at the Autumnal Equinox).
- three months later, the Sun will be seen at sunrise at the beginning of Winter, rising on the Tropic of Cancer (at the Winter Solstice).
- three months later, the Sun will be seen at sunrise at the beginning of Spring, rising on the Equator again (at the Vernal Equinox).
- three months later, the Sun will be seen at sunrise at the beginning of Summer, rising on the Tropic of Capricorn (at the Summer Solstice).
- three months later, the Sun will be seen at sunrise again at the beginning of Autumn, rising once again on the Equator (at the next Autumnal Equinox).

This 12 month Autumnal Equinox to Autumnal Equinox cycle from the beginning of one Autumn to the beginning of the next Autumn defines a solar year in the Southern hemisphere.

Because Earth is tilted at an angle of 23 and one half degrees (at what is known as the angle of obliquity), and is revolving around the Sun, we get the seasons on Earth.

In the Northern hemisphere, at the:

- Vernal Equinox, the Sun's rays are shining on Earth directly on the Equator. We get equal amounts of light and darkness, heat and cold causing Earth to warm up from Winter.

- Summer Solstice, it can be said that the Northern hemisphere of Earth is leaning (tilted) towards the Sun, so the Sun's rays are shining directly on the Tropic of Cancer. We get more light than darkness, more heat than cold. It is hot in Summer.
- Autumnal Equinox, the Sun's rays are shining on Earth directly on the Equator again. We get equal amounts of light and darkness, heat and cold causing Earth to cool down from Summer.
- Winter Solstice, it can be said that the Northern hemisphere of Earth is leaning (tilted) away from the Sun, so the Sun's rays are shining directly on the Tropic of Capricorn. We get more darkness than light, more cold than heat. It is cold in Winter.

In the Southern hemisphere, the seasons occur opposite the seasons in the Northern hemisphere. In the Southern hemisphere, at the:

- Autumnal Equinox, the Sun's rays are shining on Earth directly on the Equator. We get equal amounts of light and darkness, heat and cold causing Earth to cool down from Summer.
- Winter Solstice, it can be said that the Southern hemisphere of Earth is leaning (tilted) away from the Sun, so the Sun's rays are shining directly on the Tropic of Cancer. We get more darkness than light, more cold than heat. It is cold in Winter.
- Vernal Equinox, the Sun's rays are shining on Earth directly on the Equator again. We get equal amounts of light and darkness, heat and cold causing Earth to warm up from Winter.
- Summer Solstice, it can be said that the Southern hemisphere of Earth is leaning (tilted) toward the Sun, so the Sun's rays are shining directly on the Tropic of Capricorn. We get more light than darkness, more heat than cold. It is hot in Summer.

If one lives on the Equator, there are no seasons because the Equator is not tilted toward or away from the rays of the Sun as Earth revolves around the Sun, and there is always an equal amount of light and darkness each day of the year.

Please note that from this point on in this book, I will be presenting information from the perspective of the Northern hemisphere.

It takes 365.242189 solar days for the Vernal Equinox to Vernal Equinox cycle to occur, and this is a solar year. A tropical year, commonly used in Tropical Astrology, is equal to a solar year (the word tropical comes from the "Tropic" of Cancer and the "Tropic" of Capricorn). As a solar (tropical) year always starts at zero degrees Aries on the Vernal Equinox, it does not take precession into account.

Although a sidereal year is different from a solar year, and a sidereal year is approximately 20 solar minutes longer than a solar year, every astute astrologer knows they both start at 00:00:00 when the Sun rises at zero degrees latitude on the Equator at the Vernal Equinox. As sidereal years advance from the Vernal Equinox, the Sun will be seen from Earth at sunrise to be less and less positioned with stars in the constellation Pisces. In approximately 350 solar years, when a sidereal year begins at the Vernal Equinox, the Sun will be seen from Earth at sunrise to be positioned with the stars in the constellation Aquarius. The difference in where we see the sun rising at the Vernal Equinox now in Pisces and when we will see the sun rising in Aquarius is due to precession. A sidereal year takes precession into account.

————

A calendar year in our contemporary Gregorian calendar is based on a solar tropical year and it consists of 365.2425 solar days. It starts at 00:00:00 but on January 1st of each solar year, not on the Vernal Equinox.

Chapter 3

A SIDEREAL DAY AND
A SOLAR DAY

———

A sidereal day is the time it takes for Earth to rotate 360 degrees on its axis so that a star appears at the same position in the sky the next day. A sidereal day lasts from when a distant star is seen at a meridian longitude line on Earth until it is seen at the same meridian longitude line on Earth the next day. A sidereal day lasts 23 hours and 56 minutes.

A solar day lasts from when the Sun is seen at the noon meridian (highest point overhead in the sky) from a place on Earth until it is seen at the noon meridian again on Earth from that same place the next day. It takes 24 hours for this to occur because while Earth is rotating on its axis, Earth is also simultaneously orbiting the Sun. It takes a little longer (24 hours as opposed to 23 hours and 56 minutes) for the Sun to be seen at the noon meridian again the next day from the same place because of Earth's ongoing orbit around the Sun.

A solar day then is slightly longer than a sidereal day. In one solar 24 hour day, we can say that Earth must rotate a little more than 360 degrees to complete a solar day. Earth rotates an extra 0.986 degrees between a solar crossing at the noon meridian as seen from the same place on Earth. In 24 hours of solar time, Earth rotates 360.986 degrees.

Likewise for the Moon. The Moon must revolve around Earth more than 360 degrees in a lunar (synodic) period of approximately 3 weeks because Earth is simultaneously revolving around the Sun. A synodic period is the time from a new

Moon to the next new Moon. Because of Earth's ongoing orbit around the Sun, the Moon must revolve more than 360 degrees around Earth in a synodic period until it is again in direct line with the Sun at the next new Moon.

So we see that a sidereal day of 23 hours and 56 minutes of solar time is about 4 solar minutes less than a solar day which is 24 hours. An example of the time difference between a sidereal and solar day is when we see, on our solar civil time clock or watch, the stars rise in the East four minutes earlier each solar day, and the stars set in the West four minutes earlier each solar day. The stars rise and set on a sidereal time star-based schedule. A star or constellation will be at precisely the same position in the sky 4 minutes earlier each successive solar day. In the course of a month, this daily 4 minute shift adds up to a two hour difference in the rising time of a star or constellation. A star or constellation directly overhead at 10 p.m. on October 1 will be directly overhead at 8 p.m. on November 1. Western Sidereal Astrology utilizes the sidereal hours, minutes and seconds in a sidereal day to determine the sidereal times at which planets and stars, from a place on Earth, rise on the Eastern horizon, culminate at the Midheaven (reach the highest point in the sky), set on the Western horizon, and anti-culminate at the IC (reach the point opposite the Midheaven).

Chapter 4

WESTERN SIDEREAL ASTROLOGY AND TROPICAL ASTROLOGY

———

Many current astrologers use Tropical Astrology which is based on a tropical year (solar year) that occurs from one Vernal Equinox on Earth to the next Vernal Equinox on Earth, as Earth revolves around the Sun. Specifically, a Vernal or Spring Equinox is when, in the Northern Hemisphere, the Sun rises in the East at zero degrees latitude on the Equator, typically on March 20 or 21 in our Gregorian calendar. Just as with a solar year, a tropical year is the mean (average) solar time taken for the Sun to appear at a Vernal Equinox again.

Tropical Astrology is synchronized with solar, tropical time, and it has the Sun rising on the Vernal Equinox every year at zero degrees Aries, as the Sun did in 221 AD. The effect of precession is not taken into account, and neither is precession taken into account by our contemporary, standardized system of solar time-keeping used throughout the world. In the Northern Hemisphere, the Gregorian calendar we use, upon which the civil time shown on our clocks and watches is based, always shows Summer as being in July and August associated with the signs Cancer and Leo. If our calendar did note the effect of precession, after a few thousand years, the accumulated shift due to precession would show our Summer occurring in the months of May and June associated with the signs Taurus and Gemini instead of in our well known Summer months July and August associated with the signs Cancer and Leo. Because a solar, tropical, Gregorian year does not take precession into account, there is no backward shift in our Summer months. The same applies to conventional Tropical Astrology. The Summer months of July and August in the Northern hemisphere are always seen to occur in the signs of Cancer and Leo advanced from the Spring Vernal Equinox, which is always seen to occur at zero degrees Aries at the end of March.

In the standardization of time, it is indeed necessary to show that Summer in the Northern Hemisphere always occurs in July and August in the signs of Cancer and Leo. Our modern way of living would be impossible without standardized solar time. In astrology however we can note the effect of precession as we aren't running to catch a flight at a scheduled standardized solar time (even though we know of course how to live in that world). Astrology might consider what actually occurs in the sky due to precession, and not depend on being in synch with the arbitrary standardization of solar time indicated in our Gregorian calendar and on our clocks and watches. Precession is a natural part of how our solar system functions and its effects should be taken into account by astrologers. More and more tropical astrologers are using precession-adjusted charts to include the effects of precession in their work. Western Sidereal Astrology includes the effects of precession to currently see the Sun rising at the Vernal Equinox at the end of March at approximately 5 degrees Pisces, which is where it actually rises.

As we have already stated, Western Sidereal Astrology starts the year at 00:00:00 when the Vernal Equinox occurs, but the Sun is seen from Earth to be where it really is in relation to the stars when it rises on the Equator on the Vernal Equinox, instead of always being said to rise at zero degrees Aries on the Vernal Equinox as accepted by Tropical Astrology. For the birth time, birth day and place of a birth or event, Western Sidereal Astrology sees planetary bodies from Earth at exact sidereal times to be rising, culminating at the Midheaven, setting, and anti-culminating at the IC based on the Local Sidereal Time (LST) of the birth or event.

Due to precession, your conventional Tropical Astrology sun sign may not be your Western Sidereal Astrology sun sign. You would have to subtract 24 degrees 4 minutes and 35 seconds (this amount of precession noted on July 26, 2015 after 1,794 years from 221 AD) from your Tropical Astrology sun sign to get your Western Sidereal Astrology sun sign, and that may put your sun sign into the previous sun sign. The same applies to all the other signs of the planets in your conventional

Tropical Astrology chart and to the signs of the house cusps in that chart. You would have to subtract the same amount of precession from each of them to get their sidereal signs.

The birthchart of Person F on the next page shows the Tropical Astrology chart that does not take precession into account.

Person F - Natal Chart. Feb. 7, 1950. 12:45 PM, EST +05:00:00, Brooklyn, NY, USA, LST: 22:41:00, Geocentric, *Tropical*, Campanus, True Node.

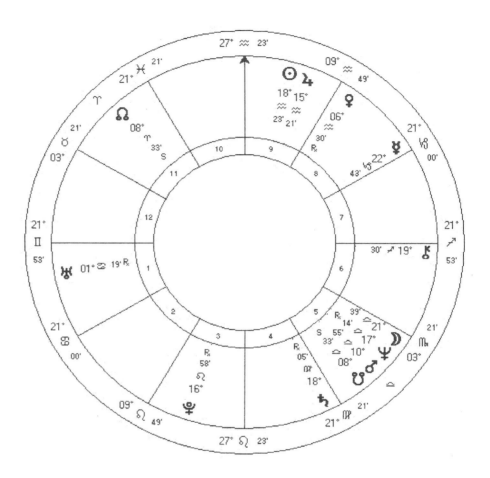

The birthchart of Person G below shows the Western Sidereal Astrology (Fagan-Bradley) chart that does take precession into account. The difference between the planet signs and house cusp signs in this chart compared to the Tropical Astrology chart on the previous page is due to the effect of precession.

Person G. Natal Chart. Feb. 7, 1950. 12:45:00 PM, EST +05:00:00, Brooklyn, NY, USA, Geocentric, Western *Sidereal* (Fagan-Bradley), Campanus, True Node.

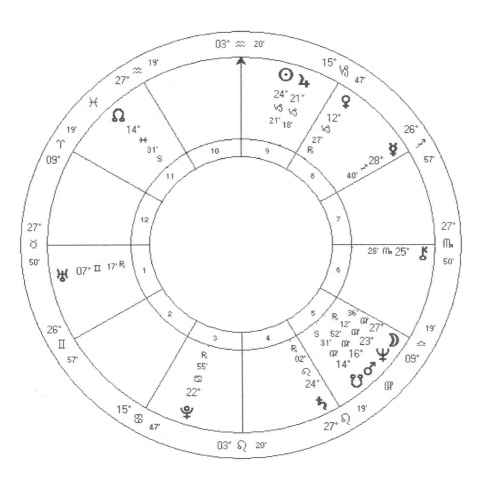

There is also another major difference between Tropical Astrology and Western Sidereal Astrology. Zodiacal and ecliptic-based Tropical Astrology looks at the planetary bodies of our solar system from Earth as seen to be in front of the circular background of the twelve constellations of the zodiac, which appear one after another in the circular ecliptic band that surrounds the Sun. In the ecliptic, the planets are located on celestial longitude lines in degrees, minutes and seconds. The planets are also located on celestial latitude lines within the ecliptic to show how far above or below they are from the plane of the ecliptic.

Equatorial-based Western Sidereal Astrology ("equatorial" because of its emphasis on Earth's Equator) looks at the planetary bodies from Earth from a different perspective involving Right Ascension and Declination. We all know about longitude and latitude lines on Earth. Put simply, longitude lines run between the North Pole and the South Pole, and places on Earth are located on lines of longitude east and west of the Prime Meridian in Greenwich England which has zero degrees of longitude. Lines of longitude intersect the Equator at points east and west of the Prime Meridian. Lines of latitude run north and south of the Equator and are parallel to it. The point at which a particular longitude line crosses a particular latitude line is a particular place on Earth.

Now visualize that these longitude and latitude lines on Earth are pushed out into outer space. These lines then become known as celestial longitude lines and celestial latitude lines. The Equator pushed out into outer space becomes the Celestial Equator. The North Pole becomes the celestial North Pole and the South Pole becomes the celestial South Pole. The Prime Meridian longitude line extended into outer space becomes a celestial line of longitude that slices through the Ecliptic at the Vernal Equinox point on the Ecliptic. It is imperative to know that at that Vernal Equinox point, the Ecliptic intersects the Celestial Equator.

Just as we can say that solar civil time on Earth is measured in time zones from the Prime Meridian in Greenwich England, we can also say that sidereal time is measured in sidereal hours, minutes and seconds along the Celestial Equator, starting from where the Vernal Equinox point intersects the Celestial Equator. This can be understood by learning about Right Ascension.

We all know that the Sun, planets and stars rise in the east and set in the west for anyone in the Northern hemisphere or the Southern hemisphere. But if we are located in the Northern hemisphere and we have the Sun, for example, in our line of sight during the day, the Sun appears to rise from our left, ascend in the sky, and then set to our right. This is known as Right Ascension. If we are located in the Southern hemisphere and we have the Sun in our line of sight during the day, the Sun appears to rise from our right, ascend in the sky, and then set to our left.

Now for a particular date and time of a birth or event on Earth at a particular location on Earth, each planet in outer space is located at a point on a particular line of celestial longitude that is crossed by a particular line of celestial latitude. From the Vernal Equinox point on the left where the Ecliptic intersects the Celestial Equator, we measure the distance to a point to the right on the Celestial Equator at which the line of celestial longitude straight down or up from a planet hits the Celestial Equator. The distance between the Vernal Equinox point and the point at which the line of celestial longitude hits the Celestial Equator is expressed in sidereal hours, minutes and seconds and it is the Right Ascension (RA) value of that planet.

The Declination value of the planet is simply the celestial line of latitude value of the planet that indicates how far above or below the planet is from the Celestial Equator. Declination is expressed in degrees, minutes and seconds.

Chapter 5

THE FUNDAMENTALS OF WESTERN SIDEREAL ASTROLOGY

———

Right Ascension and Declination are the cornerstones of Western Sidereal Astrology. You can get the daily Right Ascension (RA) and Declination values of planets from The American Sidereal Ephemeris.

At the time and place of a birth or event, the Right Ascension and Declination values of the planets are involved in calculating the sidereal times at which the planets rise in the East, culminate at the Midheaven, set in the West, and anti-culminate at the IC

For the birth or event, to determine the sidereal time when a planet is:

- on the Midheaven, the Right Ascension value (RA) of the planet is the sidereal time.
- on the IC (opposite point of the Midheaven), the Right Ascension (RA) value plus 12 is the sidereal time.
- rising in the east, the sidereal time is the Right Ascension value (RA) of the planet minus the diurnal semi-arc (d.s.a) of the planet. The diurnal arc of a planet is the amount of arc the planet is in the sky from sunrise to sunset, so half of the arc from the eastern horizon to the Midheaven is the planet's diurnal semi-arc. You can calculate the d.s.a. of the planet which includes the declination value of the planet. A planet rising on the Equator has no declination because there is no latitude on the Equator.

- setting in the west, the sidereal time is the Right Ascension value (RA) of the planet plus the diurnal semi-arc (d.s.a) of the planet. The diurnal arc of a planet is the amount of arc the planet is in the sky from sunrise to sunset, so half of the arc from the Midheaven to the western horizon is the planet's diurnal semi-arc. You can calculate the d.s.a. of the planet which includes the declination value of the planet. A planet setting on the Equator has no declination because there is no latitude on the Equator.

For examples of calculating rising and setting sidereal times, please see the Appendix which consists of the following eight sections:

- In the Northern hemisphere, the sidereal time is calculated for North Declination Mercury rising at a birth time, date and place of a birth or event.
- In the Northern hemisphere, the sidereal time is calculated for North Declination Mercury setting at a birth time, date and place of a birth or event.
- In the Northern hemisphere, the sidereal time is calculated for South Declination Mercury rising at a birth time, date and place of a birth or event.
- In the Northern hemisphere, the sidereal time is calculated for South Declination Mercury setting at a birth time, date and place of a birth or event.
- In the Southern hemisphere, the sidereal time is calculated for North Declination Mercury rising at a birth time, date and place of a birth or event.
- In the Southern hemisphere, the sidereal time is calculated for North Declination Mercury setting at a birth time, date and place of a birth or event.
- In the Southern hemisphere, the sidereal time is calculated for South Declination Mercury rising at a birth time, date and place of a birth or event.
- In the Southern hemisphere, the sidereal time is calculated for South Declination Mercury setting at a birth time, date and place of a birth or event.

The sidereal times of the planets specify when the planets at the birth or event will rise in the East, culminate at the Midheaven, set in the West, and anti-culminate at the IC. These sidereal times are shown in a "speculum" of the birth or event. Shown on the next page is an example of a speculum:

Person T. Speculum. Feb 14, 1950. 12:45 PM, EST +05:00:00, Brooklyn, NY, USA, Geocentric, Western Sidereal (Fagan-Bradley) Campanus, True Node.

```
RAMC 336 29' 29"                    LST 22:25:57
Diurnal Events: Planet on Angle
Sidereal Time

Planet/Star             Rise       Mc        Set        Ic
Sun                   16:36:49  21:50:59   3:05:09    9:50:59
Moon                  15:42:53  20:07:58   0:33:03    8:07:58
Mercury               15:22:38  20:08:34   0:54:30    8:08:34
Venus                 14:57:41  20:17:05   1:36:30    8:17:05
Mars                   6:50:02  12:45:44  18:41:26    0:45:44
Jupiter               16:17:01  21:18:43   2:20:25    9:18:43
Saturn                 4:54:03  11:17:53  17:41:44   23:17:53
Uranus                22:36:33   6:05:07  13:33:42   18:05:07
Neptune                7:23:47  13:05:46  18:47:45    1:05:46
Pluto                  1:59:24   9:27:56  16:56:27   21:27:56
Moon's North Node     18:18:59   0:30:11   6:41:24   12:30:11
```

In this speculum, each planet is shown in a row, and the Rise, Mc, Set and Ic columns are to the right of each planet. In the columns for each planet are the sidereal times at which the planet will rise in the East on the Ascendant angle (1st house cusp) of the chart of the birth or event, culminate at the Midheaven angle (10th house cusp) of the chart of the birth or event, set in the West on the Descendant angle (7th house cusp) of the chart of the birth or event, and anti-culminate at the IC angle (4th house cusp) of the chart of the birth or event.

The four sidereal times to the right of a planet show when the four angles are on the planet (as seen in the birthchart), or as we say, "directed" to the planet. For example, when a planet is rising at a sidereal time, the Ascendant is directed to that planet at that sidereal time. As sidereal time ticks forward from the LST of the birth or event, all the angles in the speculum will be directed to all the planets listed in the speculum.

To display the speculum for a person, bring up Janus, open the person's chart, go to the Calculate dropdown, and select Diurnal Events (Parans) to display the pop up box. Then in the pop up box, go to the Settings dropdown, select Options, click on Planet on Angle, and click on OK. The speculum for the person will display.

You can also add stars to the speculum. From the Settings dropdown, click on Star Selection. Then scroll down and click a checkmark in the checkbox to the left of the star you want to add to the speculum, which will be added to the bottom of the list of planets together with its sidereal times. You can then select more stars. When all the stars you want are selected, click OK. All the selected stars will be listed in the speculum.

The LST of 22:25:57 displayed at the top of the speculum is particular to the moment and place of the birth or event. Even the LST values of the births of twins will be different as each twin is born at a different minute. The LST time line that cuts through the location (the L in LST) of a birth or event is the line of longitude converted to sidereal hours, minutes and seconds. Expressed in sidereal time at that locality, it is the Midheaven of the birth or event because as the line is drawn between the North Pole and the South Pole, it cuts through the highest point in the sky (the Midheaven) at the sidereal time of the birth or event.

In creating the sidereal chart of a birth or event, the LST of the birth or event is calculated from the sidereal time given at midnight at the Prime Meridian in Greenwich England at the beginning of the day of the birth or event, along with the actual time of the birth or event, along with the longitude of the location of the birth or event. The resulting LST is then used to calculate the Ascendant, Midheaven, Descendant and IC, non-angular house cusps, and locations of the planets in the sidereal birthchart, hence the LST is the foundation of the sidereal chart.

Let's take another step forward. When for example an Mc column (Midheaven angle) sidereal time for a planet listed in the speculum becomes the LST, the Midheaven angle is directed to that planet. The planet is on the Midheaven angle in the chart of the birth or event. Each sidereal time in each angle column for a planet in the speculum will indicate when the angle will be on (directed to) the planet. When each direction occurs, the sidereal time of the direction is being used instead of the original LST of the birth or event. It is as if the sidereal time of the direction has replaced the original LST of the birth or event. When the sidereal time has replaced the LST, the angle is directed to the planet and the planet is on that angle.

We can get the amount of time needed for an angle to be directed to a planet from the LST time (that is, how much time must pass forward from the original LST time to the time of the direction) by subtracting the LST time from the sidereal time of the angle shown to the right of the planet. The difference in time is known as the arc of direction.

In the speculum on the previous page, you can see the 22:25:57 LST at the top, and in the left corner 336 degrees 29 minutes and 29 seconds of RAMC. The term RAMC means the Right Ascension of the Medium Coeli, or in modern usage, the Right Ascension of the Midheaven of the birth or event. It is pronounced "RamSee" and it is used in Western Sidereal Astrology several ways. In each way, it is a representation of the Midheaven of a birth or event.

First, the RAMC value in the top left is the LST in degrees, minutes and seconds. The conversion from the LST in sidereal time to the RAMC value in degrees, minutes and seconds is shown under the speculum of Person C below.

The LST of a birth or event is also known as the RAMC of the birth or event. Also, each of the sidereal times to the right of a listed planet in a speculum is called a RAMC of that planet, thus all the sidereal times of all the angles in the columns for the listed planets in a speculum are simply called RAMCs. In the vernacular of Western Sidereal Astrology, it is said for example that a planet rises with a particular RAMC (e.g. when the Ascendant is directed to the planet) when that RAMC (sidereal time) in the Rise column for the planet is on the RAMC (LST or Midheaven) of the birth or event.

Person C. Speculum. July 13 1973. 3:15 PM, EDT +04:00:00, Woodside, NY, USA, Geocentric, Western Sidereal (Fagan-Bradley), Campanus, True Node.

RAMC 161 23' 02"		LST 10:45:32		
Diurnal Events: Planet on Angle				
Sidereal Time				
Planet/Star	Rise	Mc	Set	Ic
Sun	0:11:50	7:31:58	14:52:05	19:31:58
Moon	13:43:02	18:13:59	22:44:56	6:13:59
Mercury	1:14:57	8:10:47	15:06:36	20:10:47
Venus	2:14:41	9:17:23	16:20:05	21:17:23
Mars	18:48:05	0:57:53	7:07:41	12:57:53
Jupiter	15:54:52	20:47:43	1:40:34	8:47:43
Saturn	22:27:39	5:50:18	13:12:58	17:50:18
Uranus	7:35:09	13:11:17	18:47:26	1:11:17
Neptune	11:24:06	16:13:19	21:02:32	4:13:19
Pluto	5:43:33	12:33:40	19:23:46	0:33:40
Moon's North Node	13:59:58	18:33:34	23:07:11	6:33:34
Aldebaran	21:38:10	4:37:16	11:36:23	16:37:16

Calculation of the RAMC value expressed in degrees, minutes and seconds of longitude at the top left of the speculum from the 10:45:32 LST (Local Sidereal Time) in hours, minutes and seconds

Given:

- One hour of time equals 15 degrees of longitude.
- There are 24 hours in a day.
- There are 360 degrees in the rotation of Earth in one day.
- 360 degrees = 24 hours X 15.
- The RAMC in degrees = LST in hours X 15.

Calculation (provided by Mark Griffin at Astrology House, New Zealand):

10:45:32 in the speculum above

10 hours 45 mins 32 secs

10 hours 45.53333 mins (32 secs / 60 = 0.53333 mins)

10.758888 hours (45.53333 mins / 60 = 0.758888 hours)

10.758888 hours x 15

161.38332 degrees

161 degrees 23.00 mins (0.38332 x 60 = 23.00 mins)

161 degrees 23 mins 00 secs

RAMC value at the top left of the speculum above

It can be visualized that successive particular sidereal times or RAMCs will be replacing the LST of the chart as time passes by, thus allowing each angle, one after the other, to be directed to each planet at each of the sidereal times (RAMCs) to the right of each planet listed in the speculum. As sidereal time increases from the LST of the birth or event, it might appear that a planet is moving clockwise to an angle, but that angle is really moving counter-clockwise to the planet (the angle is being directed to the planet).

In the following illustrations using Person T, you can see that with the passing of both solar time and sidereal time, the Descendant angle will be directed to Person T's Jupiter so that Jupiter will be on his Descendant.

The birth chart of Person T below has the time of birth 12:45 PM. Person T's Jupiter is near the 9th house cusp and far away from the Desc angle.

Person T. Natal Chart. Feb. 14, 1950. 12:45:00 PM, EST +05:00:00, Brooklyn, NY, USA. Geocentric, Western Sidereal (Fagan-Bradley), Campanus, True Node.

The speculum of Person T's birth below has the LST of 22:25:57:

Person T. Speculum. Feb 14, 1950. 12:45 PM, EST +05:00:00, Brooklyn, NY, USA, Geocentric, Western Sidereal (Fagan-Bradley) Campanus, True Node.

```
RAMC 336 29' 29"                    LST 22:25:57
Diurnal Events: Planet on Angle
Sidereal Time

Planet/Star           Rise        Mc        Set        Ic
Sun                16:36:49  21:50:59   3:05:09    9:50:59
Moon               15:42:53  20:07:58   0:33:03    8:07:58
Mercury            15:22:38  20:08:34   0:54:30    8:08:34
Venus              14:57:41  20:17:05   1:36:30    8:17:05
Mars                6:50:02  12:45:44  18:41:26    0:45:44
Jupiter            16:17:01  21:18:43   2:20:25    9:18:43
Saturn              4:54:03  11:17:53  17:41:44   23:17:53
Uranus             22:36:33   6:05:07  13:33:42   18:05:07
Neptune             7:23:47  13:05:46  18:47:45    1:05:46
Pluto               1:59:24   9:27:56  16:56:27   21:27:56
Moon's North Node  18:18:59   0:30:11   6:41:24   12:30:11
```

The second chart on the following page shows what happens 15 minutes later at 1 PM.

The new LST time has increased to 22:41:00. You can see that Person T's Jupiter is closer to the Descendant (Desc) of the chart, but actually the Desc is moving counter-clockwise closer to Person T's Jupiter, which means that the Desc is in the process of being directed to Person T's Jupiter.

Person T. Natal Chart fifteen minutes later, Feb. 14, 1950. 1:00 PM, EST +05:00:00, Brooklyn, NY, USA, Geocentric, Western Sidereal (Fagan-Bradley), Campanus, True Node.

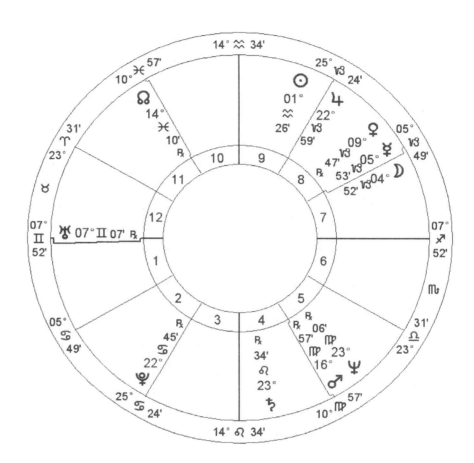

The next chart shows that at 4:39 PM, which is 3 hours and 54 minutes past the 12:45 PM birthtime of Person T, the Desc will be directed to Person T's Jupiter or we can say Jupiter will be on the Desc in Mr. T's birthchart (as shown) or that Jupiter is setting in the western horizon at the new LST of 2:20:36 at the solar time of 4:39 PM.

In the speculum following the chart, at solar time 4:39 PM, the sidereal time 2:20:36 in the Set (Descendant) column for Jupiter is the new LST of 2:20:36 for Person T. When the 2:20:36 sidereal time in the Set (Desc) column for Jupiter is the new 2:20:36 LST that replaces the natal 22:55:57 LST of person T's birth, Jupiter will be setting.

Person T - 3 hours and 54 minutes after the 12:45 PM birth. Feb. 14, 1950. 4:39 PM, EST +05:00:00, Brooklyn, NY, USA, Geocentric, Western Sidereal (Fagan-Bradley), Campanus, True Node.

You can see Jupiter on the Descendant.

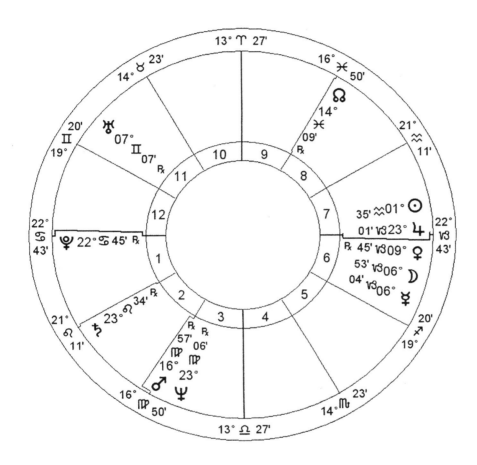

At 4:39 PM, the RAMC of 2:20:36 in the Jupiter set column has replaced the original 22:25:57 LST (RAMC) of Person T's birth as shown below:

Person T. Speculum. Feb. 14, 1950. 3 hours and 54 minutes after the 12:45 PM birth, which is 4:39 PM, EST +05:00:00, Brooklyn, NY, USA Geocentric, Western Sidereal (Fagan-Bradley), Campanus, True Node.

```
RAMC 35 09' 06"                    LST 2:20:36
Diurnal Events: Planet on Angle
Sidereal Time

Planet/Star              Rise        Mc         Set         Ic
Sun                    16:37:14   21:51:37    3:05:59     9:51:37
Moon                   15:49:39   20:17:11    0:44:43     8:17:11
Mercury                15:23:23   20:09:23    0:55:23     8:09:23
Venus                  14:57:36   20:16:56    1:36:17     8:16:56
Mars                    6:50:00   12:45:43   18:41:26     0:45:43
Jupiter                16:17:07   21:18:52    2:20:36     9:18:52
Saturn                  4:54:00   11:17:51   17:41:42    23:17:51
Uranus                 22:36:32    6:05:06   13:33:41    18:05:06
Neptune                 7:23:47   13:05:46   18:47:44     1:05:46
Pluto                   1:59:23    9:27:55   16:56:27    21:27:55
Moon's North Node      18:18:56    0:30:07    6:41:18    12:30:07
Aldebaran              21:36:59    4:35:56   11:34:52    16:35:56
```

Jupiter will be angular on the Desc (i.e. the Desc will be directed to Jupiter) which is one of the four angles of the chart. Each of the other three angles of the chart will be directed to Jupiter at the three other sidereal times provided in the row of Jupiter. It follows that the other planets in the rows of Person T's speculum will also have the four angles directed to them at the four sidereal times shown to their right.

––––––––

To summarize, each sidereal time in the speculum Rise, Mc (culminating), Set, Ic (anti culminating) columns specifies when the Ascendant (Asc), Midheaven (MC), Descendant (Desc) and IC angle will be directed to each listed planet. In the span of sidereal time starting from the LST, all the angles will have been directed to all the listed planets in the speculum.

We can say also, that when the:

- Asc is directed to a planet at a sidereal time that replaces the LST of the birth or event, that planet is rising at the eastern horizon at that sidereal time.
- MC is directed to a planet at a sidereal time that replaces the LST of the birth or event, that planet is at the Midheaven.
- Desc is directed to a planet at a sidereal time that replaces the LST of the birth or event, that planet is setting at the western horizon at that sidereal time
- IC is directed to a planet at a sidereal time that replaces the LST of the birth or event, that planet is at the point opposite the Midheaven.

The angles also have relative strengths. The Midheaven is the most powerful angle, followed by the Ascendant, then the Descendant, and then the IC. A Midheaven direction to a planet will accentuate the characteristics of that planet more than a direction of any other angle to that planet.

If the sidereal time value in a column for a planet actually equals the LST of the chart, the angle of that column is actually directed to that planet at the LST birthtime. There is no amount of time needed for that angle to be directed to that planet. The direction occurs immediately at birth if the:

- Asc column sidereal time of a planet equals the LST of the birth; that planet is on the Asc, the first house cusp, of the birthchart at birth.
- MC column sidereal time of a planet equals the LST of the birth; that planet is on the MC, the 10th house cusp of the birthchart at birth.
- Desc column sidereal time of a planet equals the LST of the birth; that planet is on the Desc, the 7th house cusp of the birthchart at birth.
- IC column sidereal time equals the LST of the birth; that planet is on the IC, the 4th house cusp of the birthchart at birth.

If you look at the sidereal birthchart of a birth showing a planet that immediately has an angle directed to it at birth, that planet can easily be seen to be at the angle in the birthchart. A planet that is angular at birth will be very powerful in the person's life, and if it is dignified, it will be a very positive force and will manifest very well during the person's life.

So now that you know how to interpret a speculum, let's discuss aspects between planets. In Tropical Astrology when two planets are conjunct, they are conjunct only in celestial longitude degrees on the ecliptic (zodiac).

In Western Sidereal Astrology, a conjunction between two planets occurs when they have the same sidereal time at which they:

- **Rise** Their equal sidereal times are derived from their right ascension and declination values.
- **Culminate on the Midheaven** Their equal sidereal times are derived from only their right ascension values.
- **Set** Their equal sidereal times are derived from their right ascension and declination values.
- **Anti-culminate on the IC** Their equal sidereal times are derived from only their right ascension values plus 12.

These planets are truly in an in mundo (in the world) conjunction aspect to each other. In sidereal time, they are actually on each other at the same angle (that is, the same angle is directed to them), or very close if their sidereal times are not exactly equal. For example, there may be planets to which the Ascendant is being directed, at the same sidereal time or close to the same sidereal time. These planets are said to be in an in mundo conjunction at their Rise on the Ascendant.

You will see that a *sorted* speculum easily shows in mundo conjunctions, squares and oppositions between planets that have angles directed to them at equal or close sidereal times. Planets must have the same or "close to within orb" sidereal times to be in aspect to each other:

- up to 8 sidereal minutes of orb (range of sidereal time) is needed between planets for them to be in aspect to each other
- as much as up to 12 minutes is needed for the Sun and the Moon to be in aspect to each other, or to be in aspect to other planets.

The ASC (Rise), MC (Mc), DESC (Set), and IC (Ic) sidereal times listed in a sorted speculum determine whether planets are in an in mundo conjunction, opposition, or square to each other.

On the next page is the sorted speculum of Person A. To display a sorted speculum, bring up Janus, open the person's chart, go to the Calculate dropdown, and select Diurnal Events (Parans) to get the pop up box. In the pop up box, go to the Settings dropdown, select Options, click on Right Ascension, and click on OK. The sorted speculum displays.

Look down the ST (Sidereal Time) column. You can see that Person A has an in mundo conjunction of the Moon (8:07:58) and Mercury (8:08:34) at the IC angle, an in mundo conjunction of the Moon (20:07:58) and Mercury (20:08:34) at the Midheaven MC angle, an in mundo conjunction of the Moon (20:07:58) and Venus (20:17:05) at the Midheaven MC angle, and an in mundo conjunction of Mars (18:41:26) and Neptune (18:47:45) at the Desc set angle.

Person A. Sorted Speculum. Feb. 14, 1950. 12:45:00 PM, EST +05:00:00, Brooklyn, NY, USA, Geocentric, Western Sidereal (Fagan-Bradley), Campanus, True Node.

```
RAMC 336 29' 29"                    LST 22:25:57
Apparent Motion of the Planets
```

Planet/Star	Event	RA		ST	LT	Earth Long of RA
Moon's North Node	Mc	7	33	0:30:11	14:48:54	42w52
Moon	Set	8	16	0:33:03	14:51:45	42w10
Mars	Ic	11	26	0:45:44	15:04:24	38w59
Mercury	Set	13	37	0:54:30	15:13:08	36w48
Neptune	Ic	16	27	1:05:46	15:24:22	33w59
Venus	Set	24	07	1:36:30	15:55:01	26w18
Pluto	Rise	29	51	1:59:24	16:17:52	20w34
Jupiter	Set	35	06	2:20:25	16:38:49	15w19
Sun	Set	46	17	3:05:09	17:23:26	4w08
Aldebaran	Mc	68	59	4:35:56	18:53:58	18e34
Saturn	Rise	73	31	4:54:03	19:12:02	23e05
Uranus	Mc	91	17	6:05:07	20:22:54	40e51
Moon's North Node	Set	100	21	6:41:24	20:59:05	49e56
Mars	Rise	102	30	6:50:02	21:07:42	52e05
Neptune	Rise	110	57	7:23:47	21:41:22	60e31
Moon	Ic	122	00	8:07:58	22:25:25	71e34
Mercury	Ic	122	08	8:08:34	22:26:01	71e43
Venus	Ic	124	16	8:17:05	22:34:31	73e51
Jupiter	Ic	139	41	9:18:43	23:35:58	89e15
Pluto	Mc	141	59	9:27:56	23:45:10	91e34
Sun	Ic	147	45	9:50:59	0:12:05	97e19
Saturn	Mc	169	28	11:17:53	1:38:45	119e03
Aldebaran	Set	173	43	11:34:52	1:55:41	123e18
Moon's North Node	Ic	187	33	12:30:11	2:50:52	137e08
Mars	Mc	191	26	12:45:44	3:06:22	141e01
Neptune	Mc	196	27	13:05:46	3:26:20	146e01
Uranus	Set	203	25	13:33:42	3:54:11	153e00
Venus	Rise	224	25	14:57:41	5:17:57	174e00
Mercury	Rise	230	39	15:22:38	5:42:50	179w46
Moon	Rise	235	43	15:42:53	6:03:02	174w42
Jupiter	Rise	244	15	16:17:01	6:37:04	166w10
Aldebaran	Ic	248	59	16:35:56	6:55:55	161w26
Sun	Rise	249	12	16:36:49	6:56:48	161w13
Pluto	Set	254	07	16:56:27	7:16:24	156w19
Saturn	Set	265	26	17:41:44	8:01:33	144w59
Uranus	Ic	271	17	18:05:07	8:24:52	139w09
Moon's North Node	Rise	274	45	18:18:59	8:38:42	135w41
Mars	Set	280	22	18:41:26	9:01:06	130w04
Neptune	Set	281	56	18:47:45	9:07:23	128w29
Moon	Mc	302	00	20:07:58	10:27:23	108w26
Mercury	Mc	302	08	20:08:34	10:27:59	108w17
Venus	Mc	304	16	20:17:05	10:36:29	106w09
Jupiter	Mc	319	41	21:18:43	11:37:56	90w45
Pluto	Ic	321	59	21:27:56	11:47:08	88w26
Aldebaran	Rise	324	15	21:36:59	11:56:10	86w11
Sun	Mc	327	45	21:50:59	12:10:07	82w41
Uranus	Rise	339	08	22:36:33	12:55:34	71w17
Saturn	Ic	349	28	23:17:53	13:36:47	60w57

On the next page is the sorted speculum of Person B.

Look down the ST (Sidereal Time) column. You can see that Person B, among other in mundo aspects, has an in mundo square between Venus (15:23:04) at the Desc set angle and Jupiter (15:29:33) at the IC angle. The angle between the Desc and the IC is 90 degrees which is a square aspect.

Person B. Sorted Speculum. July 13, 1976. 3:15 PM, EDT +04:00:00, Woodside, NY, USA, Geocentric, Western Sidereal (Fagan-Bradley), Campanus, True Node.

RAMC 161 39' 07"   LST 10:46:36

Apparent Motion of the Planets

Planet/Star	Event	RA	ST	LT	Earth Long of RA
Sun	Rise	3 17	0:13:07	4:43:15	127e42
Venus	Rise	11 10	0:44:40	5:14:42	135e35
Pluto	Ic	15 03	1:00:12	5:30:12	139e28
Saturn	Rise	19 12	1:16:48	5:46:45	143e37
Uranus	Ic	30 59	2:03:58	6:33:47	155e24
Moon's North Node	Ic	37 14	2:28:58	6:58:43	161e39
Moon	Set	42 12	2:48:47	7:18:29	166e37
Jupiter	Mc	52 23	3:29:33	7:59:08	176e48
Mars	Rise	56 52	3:47:28	8:17:01	178w43
Aldebaran	Mc	69 22	4:37:27	9:06:51	166w13
Neptune	Ic	70 18	4:41:12	9:10:36	165w17
Pluto	Rise	94 40	6:18:40	10:47:48	140w55
Mercury	Mc	111 13	7:24:52	11:53:49	124w22
Sun	Mc	113 16	7:33:04	12:02:00	122w19
Venus	Mc	120 58	8:03:52	12:32:42	114w37
Saturn	Mc	127 00	8:27:58	12:56:45	108w35
Uranus	Rise	131 34	8:46:16	13:15:00	104w01
Moon's North Node	Rise	140 15	9:21:01	13:49:39	95w20
Moon	Ic	140 57	9:23:49	13:52:27	94w38
Mars	Mc	156 26	10:25:44	14:54:12	79w09
Jupiter	Set	158 31	10:34:05	15:02:31	77w04
Aldebaran	Set	174 09	11:36:35	16:04:50	61w26
Neptune	Rise	179 09	11:56:37	16:24:50	56w26
Pluto	Mc	195 03	13:00:12	17:28:14	40w32
Uranus	Mc	210 59	14:03:58	18:31:49	24w36
Moon's North Node	Mc	217 14	14:28:58	18:56:46	18w21
Mercury	Set	222 59	14:51:55	19:19:39	12w36
Sun	Set	223 15	14:53:01	19:20:45	12w20
Venus	Set	230 46	15:23:04	19:50:42	4w49
Jupiter	Ic	232 23	15:29:33	19:57:10	3w12
Saturn	Set	234 47	15:39:09	20:06:45	0w48
Moon	Rise	239 43	15:58:52	20:26:24	4e08
Aldebaran	Ic	249 22	16:37:27	21:04:53	13e47
Neptune	Mc	250 18	16:41:12	21:08:38	14e43
Mercury	Ic	291 13	19:24:52	23:51:51	55e38
Sun	Ic	293 16	19:33:04	0:03:58	57e41
Moon's North Node	Set	294 14	19:36:55	0:07:48	58e39
Pluto	Set	295 26	19:41:44	0:12:36	59e51
Venus	Ic	300 58	20:03:52	0:34:40	65e23
Jupiter	Rise	306 15	20:25:01	0:55:46	70e40
Saturn	Ic	307 00	20:27:58	0:58:43	71e25
Moon	Mc	320 57	21:23:49	1:54:25	85e22
Neptune	Set	321 27	21:25:47	1:56:22	85e52
Aldebaran	Rise	324 35	21:38:19	2:08:52	89e00
Mars	Ic	336 26	22:25:44	2:56:10	100e51
Mercury	Rise	359 27	23:57:49	4:27:59	123e52

On the next page is the sorted speculum of Person C.

Look down the ST (Sidereal Time) column. You can see that Person C, among other in mundo aspects, has an in mundo opposition between Uranus (18:47:26) at the Desc set angle and Mars (18:48:05) at the Asc rise angle. The angle between the Desc and the Asc is 180 degrees which is an opposition aspect.

Person C. Sorted Speculum. July 13 1973. 3:15 PM, EDT +04:00:00, Woodside, NY, USA, Geocentric, Western Sidereal (Fagan-Bradley), Campanus, True Node.

```
RAMC 161 23' 02"                    LST 10:45:32
Apparent Motion of the Planets

Planet/Star         Event    RA        ST          LT         Earth
                                                              Long
                                                              of RA

Sun                 Rise     2  57     0:11:50     4:43:02    127e39
Pluto               Ic       8  25     0:33:40     5:04:48    133e06
Mars                Mc      14  28     0:57:53     5:28:57    139e09
Uranus              Ic      17  49     1:11:17     5:42:20    142e30
Mercury             Rise    18  44     1:14:57     5:45:59    143e25
Jupiter             Set     25  08     1:40:34     6:11:31    149e50
Venus               Rise    33  40     2:14:41     6:45:33    158e21
Neptune             Ic      63  20     4:13:19     8:43:52    171w59
Aldebaran           Mc      69  19     4:37:16     9:07:45    166w00
Pluto               Rise    85  53     5:43:33    10:13:51    149w26
Saturn              Mc      87  35     5:50:18    10:20:35    147w44
Moon                Ic      93  30     6:13:59    10:44:12    141w49
Moon's North Node   Ic      98  24     6:33:34    11:03:44    136w55
Mars                Set    106  55     7:07:41    11:37:45    128w24
Sun                 Mc     112  59     7:31:58    12:01:58    122w20
Uranus              Rise   113  47     7:35:09    12:05:08    121w32
Mercury             Mc     122  42     8:10:47    12:40:40    112w37
Jupiter             Ic     131  56     8:47:43    13:17:31    103w23
Venus               Mc     139  21     9:17:23    13:47:06     95w58
Neptune             Rise   171  02    11:24:06    15:53:28     64w17
Aldebaran           Set    174  06    11:36:23    16:05:43     61w13
Pluto               Mc     188  25    12:33:40    17:02:50     46w54
Mars                Ic     194  28    12:57:53    17:27:00     40w51
Uranus              Mc     197  49    13:11:17    17:40:22     37w30
Saturn              Set    198  14    13:12:58    17:42:02     37w05
Moon                Rise   205  45    13:43:02    18:12:01     29w33
Moon's North Node   Rise   210  00    13:59:58    18:28:55     25w19
Sun                 Set    223  01    14:52:05    19:20:53     12w18
Mercury             Set    226  39    15:06:36    19:35:22      8w40
Jupiter             Rise   238  43    15:54:52    20:23:30      3e24
Neptune             Mc     243  20    16:13:19    20:41:54      8e01
Venus               Set    245  01    16:20:05    20:48:38      9e42
Aldebaran           Ic     249  19    16:37:16    21:05:47     14e00
Saturn              Ic     267  35    17:50:18    22:18:37     32e16
Moon                Mc     273  30    18:13:59    22:42:14     38e11
Moon's North Node   Mc     278  24    18:33:34    23:01:46     43e05
Uranus              Set    281  51    18:47:26    23:15:35     46e32
Mars                Rise   282  01    18:48:05    23:16:14     46e42
Pluto               Set    290  57    19:23:46    23:51:50     55e38
Sun                 Ic     292  59    19:31:58     0:03:55     57e40
Mercury             Ic     302  42    20:10:47     0:42:38     67e23
Jupiter             Mc     311  56    20:47:43     1:19:29     76e37
Neptune             Set    315  38    21:02:32     1:34:15     80e19
Venus               Ic     319  21    21:17:23     1:49:04     84e02
Aldebaran           Rise   324  32    21:38:10     2:09:47     89e13
Saturn              Rise   336  55    22:27:39     2:59:08    101e36
Moon                Set    341  14    22:44:56     3:16:22    105e55
Moon's North Node   Set    346  48    23:07:11     3:38:33    111e29
```

We can say for example that in a speculum:

- Two planets might be rising at the same sidereal time. Then they are in mundo conjunct and their equal (or nearly equal) sidereal times are both in the ASC column.
- A planet might be rising at a sidereal time while another is setting. Then they are in an in mundo opposition and one planet's sidereal time is in the ASC column while the other planet's equal (or nearly equal) sidereal time is in the DESC column.
- A planet might be culminating at the midheaven while another is setting. Then they are in an in mundo square and one planet's sidereal time is in the MC column while the other planet's equal (or nearly equal) sidereal time is in the DESC column.

The most beneficial aspects are in mundo squares between dignified benefic planets: Jupiter, Venus, Uranus, Mercury (neutral), which also may include a dignified Moon and/or Sun. Looking at a sorted speculum, you might also notice that the Moon will very often have an in mundo aspect to a planet, so the Moon is not frequently void of course. You might also want to include the sidereal times of particular stars in the sorted speculum to see if they are in any in mundo aspects to planets.

Chapter 6

PRIMARY DIRECTIONS
IN YOUR LIFE

———

In the speculum of your birth, each planet and star in each row will have each of the four angles directed to it at the four sidereal times to the right of the planet. Using a Casio fx-260 SOLAR calculator, you can calculate the amount of time it takes for an angle to be directed to a planet by noting the sidereal time of the planet from the column of the angle being directed. Then from that sidereal time shown in hours:minutes:seconds, subtract your LST in hours:minutes:seconds displayed at the top of the speculum. This will give you the amount of time during the sidereal day it will take for the direction to occur to that planet. This amount of time is known as the arc of direction. Change the hours:minutes:seconds of the arc of direction to minutes:seconds. Then change these minutes:seconds to a decimal and divide the decimal amount by four.

The result is the actual age (for example, age 7 or 53.5 (age 53 and one half) at which the angle will be directed to that planet in your life. The properties of the planet will have a tendency to manifest greatly in your life at that age. The arc of direction is the total amount of time needed for the angle to be directed to the planet you selected, and this arc of direction amount of time must be divided by four because every four minute increment in this amount of time starting from your LST is equal to one year of your life. The number of four-minute increments starting from the LST is your age at which the angle will be directed to the planet. This type of direction that occurs during a person's lifetime is known as a primary direction.

Also, the age or number of years can be added to your birthday to see the approximate year and month at which the primary direction will occur. For example, if you were born 1:00 am on January 1, 1940 and the number of years for the primary direction to occur is 53.5 years, that primary direction for you will occur on July 1, 1993 at 1:00 am. That is when the planet you selected will tend to manifest greatly in your life.

To get the first primary direction to a planet that will occur in your life and to see the actual age at which it will occur, look at your birthchart and choose the planet that, going clockwise, will hit an angle first (i.e. when that angle will be directed to it). As stated in the first paragraph above, you calculate the amount of time it takes for that angle to be directed to that planet by noting the sidereal time of the planet from the column of the angle being directed. Then from that sidereal time shown in hours:minutes:seconds, subtract your LST in hours:minutes:seconds displayed at the top of the speculum. This will give you the amount of time during the sidereal day it will take for the direction to occur to that planet. This amount of time is known as the arc of direction. Change the hours:minutes:seconds of the arc of direction to minutes:seconds. Then change these minutes:seconds to a decimal and divide the decimal amount by four to get the age at which the first primary direction occurs.

As above, to get the second primary direction to a planet that will occur in your life and to see the actual age at which it will occur, look at your birthchart and select the planet that, going clockwise, will hit an angle next (i.e. when that angle will be directed to it). Calculate the amount of time it takes for that angle to be directed to that planet by noting the sidereal time of the planet from the column of the angle being directed. Then from that sidereal time shown in hours:minutes:seconds, subtract your LST in hours:minutes:seconds displayed at the top of the speculum. This will give you the amount of time during the sidereal day it will take for the direction to occur to that planet. This amount of time is known as the arc of direction. Change the hours:minutes:seconds of the arc of direction to minutes:seconds. Then change these minutes:seconds to a decimal and divide the decimal amount by four to get the age at which the second primary direction occurs.

Note: If the LST is greater than the sidereal time value of the planet you are subtracting the LST from, just add 24:00:00 to the sidereal time value and then subtract the LST. Also, if you get an outlandish age for a primary direction, the planet you see in the chart is actually already past the angle you wanted to direct the planet to, even though it looks like the planet is coming to the angle in the chart. In this case, direct the next angle in the chart to the planet, for example, use the IC instead of the Descendant.

Following is an example of how to calculate a primary direction for a birth occurring on August 4, 1959 at 2:30 pm in Brooklyn NY. Let's do the primary direction for Mercury, when the Descendant (set) angle will be directed to Mercury in Person E's life (i.e. when Mercury in Person E's chart will hit the next angle which is the Descendant). This is when Mercury will tend to manifest greatly in Person E's life.

See the chart below and the speculum that follows. Then on the following page, calculator instructions are provided for doing the primary direction.

Person E. Natal Chart. Aug. 4, 1959. 2:30 PM, EDT +04:00:00, Brooklyn, NY, USA, Geocentric, Western Sidereal (Fagan-Bradley), Campanus, True Node.

Person E. Speculum. Aug 4, 1959. 2:30 PM, EST +04:00:00, Brooklyn, NY, USA, Geocentric, Western Sidereal (Fagan-Bradley) Campanus, True Node.

RAMC 156 08' 31"   LST 10:24:34

Diurnal Events: Planet on Angle
Sidereal Time

Planet/Star	Rise	Mc	Set	Ic
Sun	1:54:19	8:56:20	15:58:21	20:56:20
Moon	2:14:10	8:59:33	15:44:55	20:59:33
Mercury	2:14:49	8:57:17	15:39:45	20:57:17
Venus	4:52:58	11:00:06	17:07:15	23:00:06
Mars	4:15:00	10:45:55	17:16:50	22:45:55
Jupiter	10:24:20	15:21:11	20:18:02	3:21:11
Saturn	13:28:56	18:05:17	22:41:37	6:05:17
Uranus	2:16:57	9:16:05	16:15:12	21:16:05
Neptune	8:49:59	14:10:31	19:31:03	2:10:31
Pluto	3:20:27	10:38:35	17:56:43	22:38:35
Moon's North Node	6:26:22	12:19:13	18:12:04	0:19:13
Aldebaran	21:37:28	4:36:28	11:35:29	16:36:28

Casio fx-260 SOLAR calculator

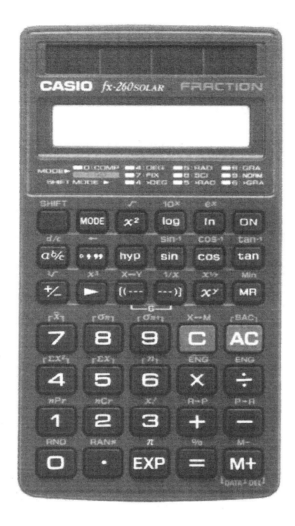

In the instructions below, to go from degrees, minutes and seconds to decimal form:

- After you enter the degrees minutes and seconds using the degrees button, hit the Shift button ▮ that's located in the upper left corner of the calculator and then the degrees button ▮ to get the decimal form of the degrees, minutes and seconds value. And when a decimal value is shown, hit the Shift button and then the degrees button to go to degrees, minutes and seconds.

To start, note the sidereal time value from the speculum for Mercury in the Descendant (Set) column which is 15h39m45s.

- Type 15 hit the degrees button [° ' "], type 39 hit the degrees button [° ' "], type 45 and then hit the subtract button [—].

Note the LST of person E's birth from the speculum, which is 10h24m34s.

- Type 10 hit the degrees button [° ' "], type 24 hit the degrees button [° ' "], type 34
- Hit the equal button [=] to get 5h15m11s.

By hand, change 5h15m11s to minutes and seconds. This equals 315m11s. Change 315m11s to a decimal and divide by 4 by doing the following:

- Type 315 hit the degrees button [° ' "], type 11
- Hit the Shift button [SHIFT] located in the upper left corner of the calculator, then hit the degrees button [° ' "] to get 315.1833333 which is the decimal.
- Hit the divide button [÷], type 4 and hit the equal button [=].

You will get 78.79583333 which rounded off is 78.8.

This is the age at which Mercury will tend to manifest greatly in Person E's life. Mercury means business, among other things. Since Person E's Mercury is in Cancer, perhaps the primary direction indicates that Person E's family house will be sold (Cancer can signify the family, the home and property). If Mars comes into play at that age, there may be a family conflict in the sale. If Venus comes into play, the sale will probably go smoothly.

A primary directed planet will tend to be manifesting greatly in your life at the age when it occurs. How well a planet manifests depends on its natal dignity or debility (this does not apply to the primary directions of stars as they have their own fixed meanings without having dignities or debilities). When the primary direction of a planet occurs, other conditions at that time such as the transits at that time, transits to the natal planets at that time, the solar return in force at that time, the lunar return in force at that time, progressed planets at that time, elevations of the planets in the chart at that time, and any other influences you may prefer to include, will also come into play (for more influences, see Advanced Predictive Techniques by K. Bowser and B. Fannin). For a primary directed star, the meaning of that star will determine how it manifests.

You must prepare in advance for the occurrence of a primary direction to be able to reap its benefits or to avoid its pitfalls. You might want to know when Saturn will tend to manifest greatly in your life so you can prepare for the challenges it will bring. You might also want to know when Jupiter will tend to manifest greatly in your life so you can take advantage of the benefits it bestows. Here are some examples of how primary directed planets will influence your life:

- *Sun* Your brilliance, willpower, creativity and vitality are revealed to the world.
- *Moon* Family, home, and health matters come to the fore - let your instincts (as well as your rationality) guide you to success.
- *Mercury* Use your mind (communication and cognition) and get moving to launch that business, college degree or project.
- *Venus* A very pleasurable and peaceful time in your life (but don't lose the beauty of the experience).
- *Mars* Ride the energy wave, stay local, and be cool (low profile).
- *Jupiter* Good luck and great times (but don't go overboard).
- *Saturn* Not such great times but if you get serious, work hard and persevere to get through the problems and delays, you will be amply rewarded.
- *Uranus* Excitement, surprises and spontaneous changes in your new, unique, independent world.
- *Neptune* Experience mysticism and spirituality, music and the arts, or drift into illusion and escapism.
- *Pluto* A major crisis; deal with it as well as you can to get through it.

You can get many more meanings of what each planet will do in your life during a primary direction from the many astrology books that describe the effects of the planets on our lives.

The use of primary directions can also be used to correct your birthtime:

- If all the major events resulting from all the primary directions of all the planets occurred a year earlier in your life, subtract 4 minutes from your birthtime to get the more accurate birthtime.
- If all the major events resulting from all the primary directions of all the planets occurred a year later in your life, add 4 minutes to your birthtime to get the more accurate birthtime.

Then when you have a more accurate birthtime, have your chart rectified by a rectification expert in astrology to confirm the new birthtime.

Appendix

To calculate the sidereal time at which the *Ascendant* is directed to a planet at a birth or event (the sidereal time at which the planet rises in the east), from the Right Ascension (RA) value of the planet, subtract the diurnal semi-arc to get the sidereal time. You have to calculate the RA of the planet at the birthtime of the birth or event, by interpolating it from the beginning RA of the planet at the birth or event day and the ending RA of the planet (the RA of the following day). The RA values for these two dates are shown in the American Sidereal Ephemeris.

You also have to calculate the declination of the planet at the birthtime of the birth or event by interpolating it from the beginning declination of the planet at the birth or event day, and the ending declination of the planet (the declination of the following day). The declination values for these two dates are shown in the American Sidereal Ephemeris.

To get the d.s.a, you must first calculate the ascensional difference (a/d) of the planet. As it rises, a planet or star, not on the Equator, forms an angle with that part of the Equator that is simultaneously rising with it. If the planet is rising on the Equator, then there is no a/d. The a/d is calculated from the following formula:

> arc sin of the a/d equals the tangent of the latitude of the place of the birth or event (i.e. the terrestrial latitude) multiplied by the tangent of the declination of the planet whose sidereal time you want.

When you arrive at the arc sin a/d which is the result of the multiplication, you must take the inverse sin of it because that is what arc sin means - the inverse of the sin. After you take the inverse of the sin, you will have the a/d.

If the place of the birth or event is in the Northern hemisphere, and the declination of the planet is north, add the a/d to 90 degrees, or if the declination of the planet is south, subtract the a/d from 90 degrees. If the place of the birth or event is in the Southern hemisphere, do the reverse; subtract the a/d from 90 degrees if the declination is north, or add the a/d to 90 degrees if the declination is south.

To calculate the sidereal time at which the *Descendant* is directed to a planet at a birth or event (the sidereal time at which the planet sets in the west), to the Right Ascension (RA) value of the planet, add the diurnal semi-arc to get the sidereal time. You have to calculate the RA of the planet at the birthtime of the birth or event, by interpolating it from the beginning RA of the planet at the birth or event day and the ending RA of the planet (the RA of the following day). The RA values for these two dates are shown in the American Sidereal Ephemeris.

You also have to calculate the declination of the planet at the birthtime of the birth or event by interpolating it from the beginning declination of the planet at the birth or event day, and the ending declination of the planet (the declination of the following day). The declination values for these two dates are shown in the American Sidereal Ephemeris.

To get the d.s.a, you must first calculate the ascensional difference (a/d) of the planet. As it sets, a planet or star, not on the Equator, forms an angle with that part of the Equator that is simultaneously setting with it. If the planet is setting on the Equator, then there is no a/d. The a/d is calculated from the following formula which most tropical and sidereal astrologers know:

> arc sin of the a/d equals the tangent of the latitude of the place of the birth or event (i.e. the terrestrial latitude) multiplied by the tangent of the declination of the planetary body.

When you arrive at the arc sin of the a/d which is the result of the multiplication, you must take the inverse of it because that is what arc sin means; the inverse of the sin. After you take the inverse of the sin, you will have the a/d.

If the place of the birth or event is in the Northern hemisphere, and the declination of the planet is north, add the a/d to 90 degrees, or if the declination of the planet is south, subtract the a/d from 90 degrees. If the place of the birth or event is in the Southern hemisphere, do the reverse; subtract the a/d from 90 degrees if the declination is north, or add the a/d to 90 degrees if the declination is south.

————

Once you get the result from either the Northern hemisphere or the Southern hemisphere, divide it by 15 to get the d.s.a.

For a rising planet, subtract the d.s.a from the RA of the planet to get the sidereal time at which the planet rises. For a setting planet, add the d.s.a to the RA of the planet to get the sidereal time at which the planet sets.

In the eight sidereal time calculation examples below, to go from degrees, minutes and seconds to decimal form:

- After entering the degrees minutes and seconds using the degrees button, hit the Shift button ▮▮▮▮ located in the upper left corner of the calculator and then hit the degrees button ▮▮▮▮ to get the decimal form of the degrees, minutes and seconds value. And when a decimal value is shown, hit the Shift button and then the degrees button to go to degrees, minutes and seconds.
- To get the arc sin of the a/d, have the value in decimal form and hit the Shift button ▮▮▮▮ and then the Sin button. The result is the a/d.

————

Examples calculating rising and setting sidereal times using the planet Mercury are provided in the following eight sections:

- In the Northern hemisphere, North declination Mercury is rising.
- In the Northern hemisphere, North declination Mercury is setting.
- In the Northern hemisphere, South declination Mercury is rising.
- In the Northern hemisphere, South declination Mercury is setting.
- In the Southern hemisphere, North declination Mercury is rising.
- In the Southern hemisphere, North declination Mercury is setting.
- In the Southern hemisphere, South declination Mercury is rising.
- In the Southern hemisphere, South declination Mercury is setting.

1. In the Northern hemisphere, calculate the sidereal time of North Declination Mercury Rising

Person L, born July 1, 2003, 2 PM, Omaha NE, 41N15'31".

```
RAMC 108 28' 51"              LST 7:13:55
Diurnal Events: Planet on Angle
Sidereal Time

Planet/Star           Rise        Mc        Set        Ic
Sun                23:13:37   6:41:29   14:09:22   18:41:29
Moon                0:54:21   8:26:15   15:58:09   20:26:15
Mercury            22:49:23   6:22:19   13:55:15   18:22:19
Venus              22:16:10   5:44:20   13:12:31   17:44:20
Mars               17:24:36  22:35:45    3:46:54   10:35:45
Jupiter             2:24:13   9:23:09   16:22:05   21:23:09
Saturn             22:49:51   6:15:31   13:41:11   18:15:31
Uranus             16:59:38  22:19:20    3:39:03   10:19:20
Neptune            16:02:40  21:00:25    1:58:10    9:00:25
Pluto              11:59:57  17:11:27   22:22:58    5:11:27
Moon's North Node  20:32:20   3:46:23   11:00:26   15:46:23
Aldebaran          21:38:18   4:39:00   11:39:41   16:39:00
```

Calculation:

ST	
	Interpolation of the RA: 2 PM is 14 hours, is 14/24 is 7/12 is .583 6 14 47 is the beginning RA and 6 24 18 is the ending RA. From 6 24 18 subtract 6 14 47 to get 9 minutes 31 seconds which is .1586 in decimal form. Multiply .583 by .1586 to get .09247 which is 5 minutes and 33 seconds. To 6 14 47, add 5 33 to get 6 20 20 which is the RA to use.
	Interpolation of the Declination: 24 8 43 is the beginning declination and 24 13 28 is the ending declination. From 24 13 28 subtract 24 8 43 to get 4 minutes and 45 seconds which is .07916 in decimal form. Multiply .583 by .07916 to get .04615 which is 2 minutes and 46 seconds. To 24 8 43 add 2 46 to get 24 11 29 which is the declination to use. Interpolation is complete.
	Arc sin a/d = (the tangent of the latitude of the place) times (the tangent of the declination of the planetary body which is Mercury in this case) 41 15 31 is 41.2586 in decimal form and the tangent of this is .87724. 24 11 29 is 24.19138 in decimal form and the tangent of this is .449237. Multiply .87724 by .449237 to get .394. The arc sin a/d of .394 is 23.209 which is 23 12 33 which is 23 h12m33s which is the a/d. **RA is 6 20 20, given is the Northern hemisphere and the declination is north, therefore:** 90 0 0 plus 23 12 33 is 113 12 33 which is 113.209 in decimal form. Divide this by 15 to get 7.54727 which is the d.s.a of 7 32 50. The RA is 6 20 20 from which you subtract the d.s.a. of 7 32 50. To perform this operation add 24 0 0 to 6 20 20 to get 30 20 20. Now from 30 20 20 subtract 7 32 50 to get 22 27 10 which is the calculated sidereal time. The difference between the calculated sidereal time 22 27 10 and the speculum sidereal time for Mercury rise which is 22 49 23 is 22 minutes and 13 seconds.

2. In the Northern hemisphere, calculate the sidereal time of North Declination Mercury Setting

Person L, born July 1, 2003, 2 PM, Omaha NE, 41N15'31".

RAMC 108 28' 51"		LST 7:13:55		
Diurnal Events: Planet on Angle				
Sidereal Time				
Planet/Star	Rise	Mc	Set	Ic
Sun	23:13:37	6:41:29	14:09:22	18:41:29
Moon	0:54:21	8:26:15	15:58:09	20:26:15
Mercury	22:49:23	6:22:19	13:55:15	18:22:19
Venus	22:16:10	5:44:20	13:12:31	17:44:20
Mars	17:24:36	22:35:45	3:46:54	10:35:45
Jupiter	2:24:13	9:23:09	16:22:05	21:23:09
Saturn	22:49:51	6:15:31	13:41:11	18:15:31
Uranus	16:59:38	22:19:20	3:39:03	10:19:20
Neptune	16:02:40	21:00:25	1:58:10	9:00:25
Pluto	11:59:57	17:11:27	22:22:58	5:11:27
Moon's North Node	20:32:20	3:46:23	11:00:26	15:46:23
Aldebaran	21:38:18	4:39:00	11:39:41	16:39:00

Calculation:

ST	
	Interpolation of the RA: 2 PM is 14 hours, is 14/24 is 7/12 is .583 6 14 47 is the beginning RA and 6 24 18 is the ending RA. From 6 24 18 subtract 6 14 47 to get 9 minutes 31 seconds which is .1586 in decimal form. Multiply .583 by .1586 to get .09247 which is 5 minutes and 33 seconds. To 6 14 47, add 5 33 to get 6 20 20 which is the RA to use. **Interpolation of the Declination:** 24 8 43 is the beginning declination and 24 13 28 is the ending declination. From 24 13 28 subtract 24 8 43 to get 4 minutes and 45 seconds which is .07916 in decimal form. Multiply .583 by .07916 to get .04615 which is 2 minutes and 46 seconds. To 24 8 43 add 2 46 to get 24 11 29 which is the declination to use. Interpolation is complete.
	Arc sin a/d = (the tangent of the latitude of the place) times (the tangent of the declination of the planetary body which is Mercury in this case) 41 15 31 is 41.2586 in decimal form and the tangent of this is .87724. 24 11 29 is 24.19138 in decimal form and the tangent of this is .449237. Multiply .87724 by .449237 to get .394. The arc sin a/d of .394 is 23.209 which is 23 12 33 which is 23 h12m33s which is the a/d. **RA is 6 20 20, given is the Northern hemisphere and the declination is north, therefore:** 90 0 0 plus 23 12 33 is 113 12 33 which is 113.209 in decimal form. Divide this by 15 to get 7.54727 which is the d.s.a of 7 32 50. The RA is 6 20 20 to which you add the d.s.a. of 7 32 50 to get 13 53 10 which is the calculated sidereal time. The difference between the calculated sidereal time 13 53 10 and the speculum sidereal time for Mercury set which is 13 55 15 is 2 minutes and 5 seconds.

3. In the Northern hemisphere, calculate the sidereal time of South Declination Mercury Rising

Person L, born Feb 18, 1990, 2 PM, Omaha NE, 41N15'31".

```
RAMC 352 35' 02"                    LST 23:30:20
Diurnal Events: Planet on Angle
Sidereal Time

Planet/Star              Rise        Mc        Set        Ic
Sun                    16:49:09   22:08:00    3:26:51   10:08:00
Moon                   12:22:15   16:36:37   20:50:58    4:36:37
Mercury                16:01:14   20:49:48    1:38:22    8:49:48
Venus                  14:30:22   19:34:53    0:39:24    7:34:53
Mars                   14:32:38   19:04:03   23:35:29    7:04:03
Jupiter                22:34:22    6:03:47   13:33:11   18:03:47
Saturn                 14:52:17   19:31:14    0:10:11    7:31:14
Uranus                 14:06:03   18:36:33   23:07:03    6:36:33
Neptune                14:21:48   18:59:14   23:36:40    6:59:14
Pluto                   9:25:55   15:18:37   21:11:19    3:18:37
Moon's North Node      16:13:24   21:15:25    2:17:26    9:15:25
Aldebaran              21:37:38    4:38:13   11:38:49   16:38:13
```

Calculation:

ST	
	Interpolation of the RA: 2 PM is 14 hours is 14/24 is 7/12 is .583. 20 44 42 is the beginning RA and 20 50 49 is the ending RA. From 20 50 49 subtract 20 44 42 to get 6 minutes 7 seconds which is .102 in decimal form. Multiply .583 by .102 to get .0594 which is 3 minutes and 34 seconds. To 20 44 42, add 3 34 to get 20 48 16 which is the RA to use. **Interpolation of the Declination:** 2 PM is 14 hours, is 14/24 is 7/12. From 12/12 subtract 7/12 to get 5/12 which is .42. 19 31 3 is the beginning declination and 19 12 58 is the ending declination. From 19 31 3 subtract 19 12 58 to get 18 minutes and 5 seconds which is .3 in decimal form. Multiply .42 by .3 to get .12658 which is 7 minutes and 36 seconds. From 19 31 3 subtract 7 36 to get 19 23 27 which is the declination to use. Interpolation is complete.
	Arc sin a/d = (the tangent of the latitude of the place) times (the tangent of the declination of the planetary body which is Mercury in this case) 41 15 31 is 41.2586 in decimal form and the tangent of this is .87724. 19 23 27 is 19.39 in decimal form and the tangent of this is .35. Multiply .87724 by .35 to get .307034. The arc sin a/d of .3 is 17.88 which is 17 52 50 which is 17 h 52 m 50 s which is the a/d. **RA is 20 48 16, given is the Northern hemisphere and the declination is south, therefore:** 90 0 0 minus 17 52 50 is 72 7 10 which is 72.12 in decimal form. Divide this by 15 to get 4.808 which is the d.s.a of 4 48 29. The RA is 20 48 16 from which you subtract the d.s.a. of 4 48 29. to get 15 59 47 which is the calculated sidereal time. The difference between the calculated sidereal time 15 59 47 and the speculum sidereal time for Mercury rise which is 16 01 14 is 1 minute and 27 seconds.

4. In the Northern hemisphere, calculate the sidereal time of South Declination Mercury Setting

Person W, born Feb 18, 1990, 2 PM, Omaha NE, 41N15'31".

RAMC 352 35' 02"		LST 23:30:20		
Diurnal Events: Planet on Angle				
Sidereal Time				
Planet/Star	Rise	Mc	Set	Ic
Sun	16:49:09	22:08:00	3:26:51	10:08:00
Moon	12:22:15	16:36:37	20:50:58	4:36:37
Mercury	16:01:14	20:49:48	1:38:22	8:49:48
Venus	14:30:22	19:34:53	0:39:24	7:34:53
Mars	14:32:38	19:04:03	23:35:29	7:04:03
Jupiter	22:34:22	6:03:47	13:33:11	18:03:47
Saturn	14:52:17	19:31:14	0:10:11	7:31:14
Uranus	14:06:03	18:36:33	23:07:03	6:36:33
Neptune	14:21:48	18:59:14	23:36:40	6:59:14
Pluto	9:25:55	15:18:37	21:11:19	3:18:37
Moon's North Node	16:13:24	21:15:25	2:17:26	9:15:25
Aldebaran	21:37:38	4:38:13	11:38:49	16:38:13

Calculation:

ST	**Interpolation of the RA:**
	2 PM is 14 hours, is 14/24 is 7/12 which is .583.
	20 44 42 is the beginning RA and 20 50 49 is the ending RA.
	From 20 50 49 subtract 20 44 42 to get 6 minutes 7 seconds which is .102 in decimal form. Multiply .583 by .102 to get .0594 which is 3 minutes and 34 seconds. To 20 44 42, add 3 34 to get 20 48 16 which is the RA to use.
	Interpolation of the Declination:
	2 PM is 14 hours, is 14/24 is 7/12. From 12/12 subtract 7/12 to get 5/12 which is .42.
	19 31 3 is the beginning declination and 19 12 58 is the ending declination.
	From 19 31 3 subtract 19 12 58 to get 18 minutes and 5 seconds which is .3 in decimal form. Multiply .42 by .3 to get .12658 which is 7 minutes and 36 seconds. From 19 31 3 subtract 7 36 to get 19 23 27 which is the declination to use.
	Interpolation is complete.
	Arc sin a/d = (the tangent of the latitude of the place) times (the tangent of the declination of the planetary body which is Mercury in this case)
	41 15 31 is 41.2586 in decimal form and the tangent of this is .87724.
	19 23 27 is 19.39 in decimal form and the tangent of this is .35.
	Multiply .87724 by .35 to get .307034.
	The arc sin a/d of .3 is 17.88 which is 17 52 50 which is 17 h52m50s which is the a/d.
	RA is 20 48 16, given is the Northern hemisphere and the declination is south, therefore:
	90 0 0 minus 17 52 50 is 72 7 10 which is 72.12 in decimal form. Divide this by 15 to get 4.808 which is the d.s.a of 4 48 29.
	The RA is 20 48 16 to which you add the d.s.a. of 4 48 29. to get 25 36 45 from which you subtract 24 0 0 to get 1 36 45 which is the calculated sidereal time.
	The difference between the calculated sidereal time 1 36 45 and the speculum sidereal time for Mercury set which is 1 38 20 is 1 minute and 37 seconds.

5. *In the Southern hemisphere, calculate the sidereal time of North Declination Mercury Rising*

Person K, born July 1, 2003, 2 PM, Montevideo Uruguay, 34S53.

```
RAMC 118 09' 10"                    LST 7:52:36
Diurnal Events: Planet on Angle
Sidereal Time

Planet/Star              Rise       Mc         Set        Ic
Sun                      1:50:21    6:41:09    11:31:56   18:41:09
Moon                     3:34:40    8:21:39    13:08:38   20:21:39
Mercury                  1:34:35    6:21:32    11:08:28   18:21:32
Venus                    0:53:17    5:43:54    10:34:30   17:43:54
Mars                     15:56:55   22:35:39   5:14:22    10:35:39
Jupiter                  4:09:45    9:23:05    14:36:25   21:23:05
Saturn                   1:22:57    6:15:28    11:08:00   18:15:28
Uranus                   15:47:23   22:19:21   4:51:18    10:19:21
Neptune                  14:11:11   21:00:25   3:49:40    9:00:25
Pluto                    10:33:02   17:11:28   23:49:54   5:11:28
Moon's North Node        22:44:54   3:46:25    8:47:57    15:46:25
Aldebaran                23:27:01   4:39:00    9:50:58    16:39:00
```

Calculation:

ST	Interpolation of the RA:
	2 PM is 14 hours, is 14/24 is 7/12 is .583
	6 14 47 is the beginning RA and 6 24 18 is the ending RA.
	From 6 24 18 subtract 6 14 47 to get 9 minutes 31 seconds which is .1586 in decimal form. Multiply .583 by .1586 to get .09247 which is 5 minutes and 33 seconds. To 6 14 47, add 5 33 to get 6 20 20 which is the RA to use.
	Interpolation of the Declination:
	24 8 43 is the beginning declination and 24 13 28 is the ending declination.
	From 24 13 28 subtract 24 8 43 to get 4 minutes and 45 seconds which is .07916 in decimal form. Multiply .583 by .07916 to get .04615 which is 2 minutes and 46 seconds. To 24 8 43 add 2 46 to get 24 11 29 which is the declination to use.
	Interpolation is complete.
	Arc sin a/d = (the tangent of the latitude of the place) times (the tangent of the declination of the planetary body which is Mercury in this case)
	34 53 is 34.883 in decimal form and the tangent of this is .69718.
	24 11 29 is 24.19138 in decimal form and the tangent of this is .449237.
	Multiply .69718 by .449237 to get .3132.
	The arc sin a/d of .3132 is 18.252 which is 18 15 8 which is 18 h15m8s which is the a/d.
	RA is 6 20 20, given is the Southern hemisphere and the declination is north, therefore:
	90 0 0 minus 18 15 8 is 71 44 52 which is 71.747 in decimal form. Divide this by 15 to get 4.783 which is the d.s.a of 4 46 59.
	The RA is 6 20 20 from which you subtract the d.s.a. of 4 46 59 to get 1 33 21 which is the calculated sidereal time.
	The difference between the calculated sidereal time 1 33 21 and the speculum sidereal time for Mercury rise which is 1 34 35 is 1 minute and 14 seconds.

6. In the Southern hemisphere, calculate the sidereal time of North Declination Mercury Setting

Person K, born July 1, 2003, 2 PM, Montevideo Uruguay, 34S53.

```
RAMC 118 09' 10"                    LST 7:52:36
Diurnal Events: Planet on Angle
Sidereal Time

Planet/Star              Rise        Mc        Set        Ic
Sun                    1:50:21   6:41:09   11:31:56   18:41:09
Moon                   3:34:40   8:21:39   13:08:38   20:21:39
Mercury                1:34:35   6:21:32   11:08:28   18:21:32
Venus                  0:53:17   5:43:54   10:34:30   17:43:54
Mars                  15:56:55  22:35:39    5:14:22   10:35:39
Jupiter                4:09:45   9:23:05   14:36:25   21:23:05
Saturn                 1:22:57   6:15:28   11:08:00   18:15:28
Uranus                15:47:23  22:19:21    4:51:18   10:19:21
Neptune               14:11:11  21:00:25    3:49:40    9:00:25
Pluto                 10:33:02  17:11:28   23:49:54    5:11:28
Moon's North Node     22:44:54   3:46:25    8:47:57   15:46:25
Aldebaran             23:27:01   4:39:00    9:50:58   16:39:00
```

Calculation:

ST	
	Interpolation of the RA: 2 PM is 14 hours, is 14/24 is 7/12 is .583 6 14 47 is the beginning RA and 6 24 18 is the ending RA. From 6 24 18 subtract 6 14 47 to get 9 minutes 31 seconds which is .1586 in decimal form. Multiply .583 by .1586 to get .09247 which is 5 minutes and 33 seconds. To 6 14 47, add 5 33 to get 6 20 20 which is the RA to use. **Interpolation of the Declination:** 24 8 43 is the beginning declination and 24 13 28 is the ending declination. From 24 13 28 subtract 24 8 43 to get 4 minutes and 45 seconds which is .07916 in decimal form. Multiply .583 by .07916 to get .04615 which is 2 minutes and 46 seconds. To 24 8 43 add 2 46 to get 24 11 29 which is the declination to use. Interpolation is complete.
	Arc sin a/d = (the tangent of the latitude of the place) times (the tangent of the declination of the planetary body which is Mercury in this case) 34 53 is 34.883 in decimal form and the tangent of this is .69718. 24 11 29 is 24.19138 in decimal form and the tangent of this is .449237. Multiply .69718 by .449237 to get .3132. The arc sin a/d of .3132 is 18.252 which is 18 15 8 which is 18 h15m8s which is the a/d. **RA is 6 20 20, given is the Southern hemisphere and the declination is north, therefore:** 90 0 0 minus 18 15 8 is 71 44 52 which is 71.747 in decimal form. Divide this by 15 to get 4.783 which is the d.s.a of 4 46 59. The RA is 6 20 20 to which you add the d.s.a. of 4 46 59 to get 11 7 19 which is the calculated sidereal time. The difference between the calculated sidereal time 11 7 19 and the speculum sidereal time for Mercury rise which is 11 8 28 is 1 minute and 9 seconds.

7. In the Southern hemisphere, calculate the sidereal time of South Declination Mercury Rising

Person U, born Feb 18, 1990, 2 PM, Montevideo Uruguay, 34S53.

RAMC 332 10' 25"		LST 22:08:41		
Diurnal Events: Planet on Angle				
Sidereal Time				
Planet/Star	Rise	Mc	Set	Ic
Sun	15:34:33	22:07:22	4:40:10	10:07:22
Moon	9:05:44	16:27:42	23:49:40	4:27:42
Mercury	13:52:11	20:48:47	3:45:22	8:48:47
Venus	12:50:43	19:34:37	2:18:31	7:34:37
Mars	11:53:46	19:03:32	2:13:17	7:03:32
Jupiter	1:14:10	6:03:48	10:53:26	18:03:48
Saturn	12:27:15	19:31:10	2:35:04	7:31:10
Uranus	11:26:05	18:36:31	1:46:58	6:36:31
Neptune	11:54:08	18:59:13	2:04:18	6:59:13
Pluto	9:12:49	15:18:37	21:24:25	3:18:37
Moon's North Node	14:29:31	21:15:25	4:01:18	9:15:25
Aldebaran	23:26:10	4:38:13	9:50:17	16:38:13

Calculation:

ST	Interpolation of the RA:
	2 PM is 14 hours, is 14/24 is 7/12 is .583
	20 44 42 is the beginning RA and 20 50 49 is the ending RA.
	From 20 50 49 subtract 20 44 42 to get 6 minutes 7 seconds which is .102 in decimal form. Multiply .583 by .102 to get .0594 which is 3 minutes and 34 seconds. To 20 44 42, add 3 34 to get 20 48 16 which is the RA to use.
	Interpolation of the Declination:
	2 PM is 14 hours, is 14/24 is 7/12. From 12/12 subtract 7/12 to get 5/12 which is .42.
	19 31 3 is the beginning declination and 19 12 58 is the ending declination.
	From 19 31 3 subtract 19 12 58 to get 18 minutes and 5 seconds which is .3 in decimal form. Multiply .42 by .3 to get .12658 which is 7 minutes and 36 seconds. To 19 31 3 add 7 36 to get 19 23 27 which is the declination to use.
	Interpolation is complete.
	Arc sin a/d = (the tangent of the latitude of the place) times (the tangent of the declination of the planetary body which is Mercury in this case)
	34 53 is 34.883 in decimal form and the tangent of this is .69718.
	19 23 27 is 19.39 in decimal form and the tangent of this is .35.
	Multiply .69718 by .35 to get ..244.
	The arc sin a/d of .244 is 14.1234 which is 14 7 22 which is 14 h7m22s which is the a/d.
	RA is 20 48 16, given is the Southern hemisphere and the declination is south, therefore:
	90 0 0 plus 14 7 22 is 104 7 22 which is 104.1227778 in decimal form. Divide this by 15 to get 6.94 which is the d.s.a of 6 56 30.
	The RA is 20 48 16 from which you subtract the d.s.a. of 6 56 30 to get 13 51 46 which is the calculated sidereal time.
	The difference between the calculated sidereal time 13 51 46 and the speculum sidereal time for Mercury rise which is 13 52 11 is 25 seconds.

8. In the Southern hemisphere, calculate the sidereal time of South Declination Mercury Setting

Person U, born Feb 18, 1990, 2 PM, Montevideo Uruguay, 34S53.

```
RAMC 332 10' 25"                    LST 22:08:41
Diurnal Events: Planet on Angle
Sidereal Time

Planet/Star              Rise       Mc       Set       Ic
Sun                   15:34:33   22:07:22   4:40:10   10:07:22
Moon                   9:05:44   16:27:42  23:49:40    4:27:42
Mercury               13:52:11   20:48:47   3:45:22    8:48:47
Venus                 12:50:43   19:34:37   2:18:31    7:34:37
Mars                  11:53:46   19:03:32   2:13:17    7:03:32
Jupiter                1:14:10    6:03:48  10:53:26   18:03:48
Saturn                12:27:15   19:31:10   2:35:04    7:31:10
Uranus                11:26:05   18:36:31   1:46:58    6:36:31
Neptune               11:54:08   18:59:13   2:04:18    6:59:13
Pluto                  9:12:49   15:18:37  21:24:25    3:18:37
Moon's North Node     14:29:31   21:15:25   4:01:18    9:15:25
Aldebaran             23:26:10    4:38:13   9:50:17   16:38:13
```

Calculation:

ST	
	Interpolation of the RA:
	2 PM is 14 hours, is 14/24 is 7/12 is .583
	20 44 42 is the beginning RA and 20 50 49 is the ending RA.
	From 20 50 49 subtract 20 44 42 to get 6 minutes 7 seconds which is .102 in decimal form. Multiply .583 by .102 to get .0594 which is 3 minutes and 34 seconds. To 20 44 42, add 3 34 to get 20 48 16 which is the RA to use.
	Interpolation of the Declination:
	2 PM is 14 hours, is 14/24 is 7/12. From 12/12 subtract 7/12 to get 5/12 which is .42.
	19 31 3 is the beginning declination and 19 12 58 is the ending declination.
	From 19 31 3 subtract 19 12 58 to get 18 minutes and 5 seconds which is .3 in decimal form. Multiply .42 by .3 to get .12658 which is 7 minutes and 36 seconds. To 19 31 3 add 7 36 get 19 23 27 which is the declination to use.
	Interpolation is complete.
	Arc sin a/d = (the tangent of the latitude of the place) times (the tangent of the declination of the planetary body which is Mercury in this case)
	34 53 is 34.883 in decimal form and the tangent of this is .69718.
	19 23 27 is 19.39 in decimal form and the tangent of this is .35.
	Multiply .69718 by .35 to get ..244.
	The arc sin a/d of .244 is 14.1234 which is 14 7 22 which is 14 h7m22s which is the a/d.
	RA is 20 48 16, given is the Southern hemisphere and the declination is south, therefore:
	90 0 0 plus 14 7 22 is 104 7 22 which is 104.1227778 in decimal form. Divide this by 15 to get 6.94 which is the d.s.a of 6 56 30.
	The RA is 20 48 16 to which you add the d.s.a. of 6 56 30 to get 27 44 46 from which you subtract 24 0 0 to get 3 44 46 which is the calculated sidereal time.
	The difference between the calculated sidereal time 3 44 46 and the speculum sidereal time for Mercury rise which is 3 45 22 is 36 seconds.

Bibliography

An Introduction to Western Sidereal Astrology, Kenneth Bowser, 2012, published by the American Federation of Astrologers, Inc., 6535 S. Rural Road, Tempe AZ 85283 which also includes a wealth of information on the planets, signs, houses, and the aspects between planets.

The American Sidereal Ephemeris, 1975-2000 and 2001-2025, compiled and programmed by Neil F. Michelsen, formatting by Gerald Peters, published by ACS Publications, 5521 Ruffin Road, San Diego, CA 92123.

Encyclopedia of Astrology, Nicholas deVore, The Philosophical Library, June 1947, New York.

For sidereal day information: http://earthsky.org/astronomy-essentials/what-is-sidereal-time.

Resources

To implement the Western Sidereal Astrology presented in this book, consider using the following resources.

Janus astrological software v4.3 or higher (for charts and speculums).
Janus Settings:
- House System: Campanus
- Coordinates: Geocentric
- Zodiac: Fagan-Bradley
- Moon's Node: True

www.myprimaries.com by John Savarese
www.westernsiderealastrology.com by Kenneth Bowser
www.ltastrology.com by Bert Fannin
Calculator: Casio fx-260 SOLAR (easy to use)

Now that you know how to calculate the sidereal times at which planets and stars rise and set on Earth using Right Ascension and Declination, you will really appreciate the NASA website www.apod.nasa.gov/apod/archivedpix.html which has really great photos of planetary bodies and events.

Notes

Notes

Notes

Notes

Notes

Notes

Printed in Great Britain
by Amazon